Developing Num

USING AND APPLYING MATHS

INVESTIGATIONS FOR THE DAILY MATHS LESSON

year
6

Hilary Koll and Steve Mills

A & C BLACK

Mathematical skills and processes

Page	Activity title	Predict	Visualise	Look for pattern	Record	Reason	Make decisions	Estimate	Explain	Be systematic	Co-operate	Compare	Test ideas	Trial and improvement	Ask own questions	Generalise	Check	Simplify
	Numbers and the number system																	
14	Square houses	○		●					○	●		○	○				○	
15	Steep signs	●	○		●				○			○	○					
16	Diluting dilemma		●	○		○			●								○	○
17	Counter acts	○	○	●	○	○			○	○			○			●		
18	Cats and dogs			○		●			○	●	○							
19	Haunted hotel			○	●				○	●						○		●
20	Chinese roots	○				○	●					○	●			○	●	
	Calculations																	
21	Crafty columns			●		○				○	○	○		○		○	○	
22	Domino magic!			○		●			○			○	●		○	●		○
23	Tennis teaser	○				○						○	○	●				
24	Party invitations			○		●		○	●				○				○	
25–26	Card shuffle: 1 and 2				○	○	○					○		●			○	
	Solving problems																	
27	Spellbound		○	●						●						○	○	○
28	How much are you worth?				○	○	●		○		●		●					
29	Always, sometimes, never		●			●		○				○				○		
30	The Wizard of Odd			○	○	○				●							○	
31	Football tables			○		○			○				●			●		
32	You've been cubed!		○	○		●			○		○							●
	Handling data																	
33	Average cards					●		○	●									
	Measures, shape and space																	
34	Digital light bars	○	○	●	○	○				●		○	○					○
35	Stick insects	○			○		●				●						○	
36–37	Curious co-ordinates: 1 and 2		●	○								○	●					
38	What's your angle?	○		○								○	●			●		
39–40	Shape shuffle: 1 and 2		●		●				○			●		○				
41	Grow-Faster Granules				○	●	○		●		○		○					●
42	Vertex variations		●	○					○			○	○					
43	Time travel						○	○		○		○	○	●		○		
44	Crazy co-ordinates		○	●					○	●								
45	Talking angles		○					○	○	●	●	○						
46	Mass hysteria	○			○				●		●		○				○	
47	Peas, please	●			○	●		○	○		●	○				○		
48	Troublesome triangles		●							●		○					○	●

● Key processes identified on the activity sheet   ○ Additional processes involved in the activity

Contents

Measures, shape and space

Published 2005 by A & C Black Publishers Limited
37 Soho Square, London W1D 3QZ
www.acblack.com

ISBN-10: 0-7136-7141-6
ISBN-13: 978-0-7136-7141-4

Copyright text © Hilary Koll and Steve Mills, 2005
Copyright illustrations © Pat Murray, 2005
Copyright cover illustration © Charlotte Hard, 2005
Editors: Lynne Williamson and Marie Lister
Designer: Heather Billin

The authors and publishers would like to thank Jane McNeill and Catherine Yemm for their advice in producing this series of books.

A CIP catalogue record for this book is available from the British Library.

Printed and bound in Great Britain by Cromwell Press Ltd, Trowbridge, Wiltshire.

A & C Black uses paper produced with elemental chlorine-free pulp, harvested from managed sustainable forests.

Introduction

Developing Numeracy: Using and Applying Maths is a series of seven photocopiable activity books designed to be used during the daily maths lesson. The books focus on using and applying mathematics, as referred to in the National Numeracy Strategy *Framework for teaching mathematics*. The activities are intended to be used in the time allocated to pupil activities during the main part of the lesson. They are designed to develop and reinforce the skills and processes that are vital to help children use and apply their maths.

Using and applying mathematics

There are several different components which make up the **content** of maths and form the bulk of any maths curriculum:

- **mathematical facts**, for example, a triangle has three sides;
- **mathematical skills**, such as counting;
- **mathematical concepts**, like place value.

For maths teaching is to be successful, it is vital that children can *use* this mathematical content beyond their classroom, either in real-life situations or as a basis for further understanding. However, in order to do so, they require extra abilities over and above the mathematical content they have learned. These extra abilities are often referred to as the **processes** of mathematical activity. It is these processes which make mathematical content usable.

As an example, consider this question:
How many triangles are there in this shape?

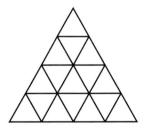

The mathematical content required is only:
- the **fact** that a triangle has three sides;
- the **skill** of counting.

As such, it could be expected that very young children could solve this problem. The fact that they cannot suggests that other abilities are involved. These are the processes, and for this question they include:
- visualising the different-sized triangles;
- being systematic in counting all the triangles of different sizes;
- looking for patterns in the numbers of triangles;
- trial and improvement;
- recording.

Unless children can apply these processes in this situation, then however good their counting skills and knowledge of triangles may be, they will fail.

The 'solving problems' strand of the *Framework for teaching mathematics* emphasises the importance of using and applying mathematics. This series of books is intended to make explicit the skills and processes involved in learning how to put maths knowledge to use.

Using and Applying Maths Year 6 supports the development of the using and applying processes by providing opportunities to introduce and practise them through a series of activities. On the whole these activities are designed for children to work on independently, although this is not always possible and occasionally some children may need support.

Pre-school children are naturally inquisitive about the world around them. They love to explore and experiment, and to make marks and record things on paper in their own idiosyncratic ways. Unfortunately, once at school the focus is often placed firmly on the maths content alone and children can be led to believe that maths is not a subject of exploration, but rather one of simply learning the 'right way to do things'. As a result, when older children are asked to explore and investigate maths they are often at a loss if their maths teaching to date has not encouraged and built upon their natural instincts.

Year 6 helps children to develop the following processes:
- predicting
- visualising
- looking for pattern
- recording
- reasoning
- making decisions
- estimating
- explaining
- being systematic
- co-operating
- comparing
- testing ideas
- trial and improvement
- asking own questions
- generalising
- checking
- simplifying

When using these activities, the focus need not be on the actual mathematical content. Instead, the teacher's demonstrations, discussions and questioning should emphasise the processes the children are using. A summary of the skills and processes covered by each activity is shown on page 2. When appropriate, invite the children to explain their thinking to others. Research has shown that children develop processes most successfully when the teacher encourages them to act as experts rather than novices, allowing them to work autonomously and encouraging a range of approaches to any problem rather than constraining discussion to produce an overall class plan. The children should evaluate their own plans against other plans in the posing, planning and monitoring phases of the lessons.

Extension

Many of the activity sheets end with a challenge (**Now try this!**) which reinforces and extends the children's learning, and provides the teacher with an opportunity for assessment. On occasion, it may be helpful to read the instructions with the children before they begin the activity. For some of the challenges the children will need to record their answers on a separate piece of paper.

Organisation

Very little equipment is needed, but it will be useful to have the following resources available: coloured pencils, counters, dice, scissors, glue, coins, squared paper, number lines and number tracks.

To help teachers select appropriate learning experiences for the children, the activities are grouped into sections within the book. However, the activities are not expected to be used in this order unless stated otherwise. The sheets are intended to support, rather than direct, the teacher's planning.

Some activities can be made easier or more challenging by masking or substituting numbers. You may wish to re-use pages by copying them onto card and laminating them.

Teachers' notes

Brief notes are provided at the foot of each page giving ideas and suggestions for maximising the effectiveness of the activity sheets. These can be masked before copying.

Solutions and further explanations of the activities can be found on pages 7–13, together with examples of questions that you can ask.

Whole class warm-up activities

The following activities provide some practical ideas which can be used to introduce the main teaching part of the lesson.

Making decisions

Start by saying: *I had £5 but I dropped 10p and it rolled away, so I had £4.90.* Ask a child to continue the story by adding or subtracting up to 50p each time: for example, *I had £4.90 and I bought some chocolate for 35p, so I had £4.55;* or *I had £4.90 and I was given 20p by my grandma, so I had £5.10.* If correct, the child can nominate someone else to continue the story.

Looking for pattern, testing ideas and explaining

On the board, draw a 4 × 5 grid with a number in each section, for example:

0·1	0·8	1·0	9·6	0·2
3	5·2	8·1	4·8	1·9
2·7	7	4·3	2	5·4
7·3	5·7	3·2	0·9	2·6

Ask the children to create number statements using the numbers in the grid: for example, $0·1 + 0·9 = 1·0$, $2 \times 4·8 = 9·6$, $9·6 \div 3 = 3·2$. (It can be useful to draw a blank grid on card and laminate it. New numbers can then be written in when required.)

Visualising

Ask the children to draw a shape or letter on a piece of paper:

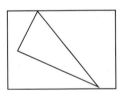

Choose a child to describe what he or she has drawn. The other children can ask questions to which the child describing the shape answers *Yes* or *No*.

Ask the children to recreate the drawing on their own piece of paper.

Being systematic

Write the number 18 on the board. Ask the children to suggest ways of adding three even numbers to make 18 (for example, $2 + 12 + 4$). After a while, introduce the idea that numbers can be used more than once (for example, $8 + 8 + 2$). List correct suggestions on the board and prompt the children to look for more: *How many twos have we written? How many eights? Are we missing any?* Begin to organise the list so that all the number sentences beginning with '2' come together, and so on (for example, $2 + 2 + 14$, $2 + 4 + 12$…).

Notes on the activities

Numbers and the number system

Square houses (page 14)

☆ *Processes: look for pattern, be systematic, predict, estimate, compare, check, test ideas*

Solutions for adding three numbers include:

1 2 2 3	$1 + 4 + 4 = 9$
2 4 4 6	$4 + 16 + 16 = 36$
3 6 6 9	$9 + 36 + 36 = 81$
4 8 8 12	$16 + 64 + 64 = 144$

(and 5 10 10 15, and so on)

1 4 8 9	$1 + 16 + 64 = 81$
2 3 6 7	$4 + 9 + 36 = 49$
4 4 7 9	$16 + 16 + 49 = 81$
2 6 9 11	$4 + 36 + 81 = 121$

Solutions for adding two numbers include:

3 4 5	$9 + 16 = 25$
6 8 10	$36 + 64 = 100$

(and 5 12 13, and so on)

When including other three-digit squares, patterns can be explored, for example:

Multiply the first two consecutive numbers to get the third, and add one to the third to get the fourth:

1 2 2 3
2 3 6 7
3 4 12 13
4 5 20 21
5 6 30 31, and so on

Double the first number to get the second and third numbers, and add the first and the second to get the fourth:

1 2 2 3
2 4 4 6
3 6 6 9
4 8 8 12
5 10 10 15
6 12 12 18, and so on

Suggested questions/prompts:

● Do you notice any patterns? Explain them.
● What strategies did you use?
● Can you extend this pattern? Use it to predict additions of larger square numbers.

Steep signs (page 15)

☆ *Processes: reason, predict, test ideas, visualise, explain, compare*

This activity helps the children to understand gradients (for example, to know that 1 : 4 means four parts across for every 1 up). The order of the signs (least steep gradient first) is 10%, 1 : 8, 1 : 7, 20%, 1 : 4.

Suggested questions/prompts:

● Tell us about what you have learned.
● Which slope was the steepest?
● Can you tell me another ratio that would be steeper than this one?

Diluting dilemma (page 16)

☆ *Processes: visualise, explain, reason, check, look for pattern, simplify*

The pattern looks like this:

Blackcurrant	Water
$\frac{1}{5}$	$\frac{4}{5}$
$\frac{1}{10}$	$\frac{9}{10}$
$\frac{1}{20}$	$\frac{19}{20}$
$\frac{1}{40}$	$\frac{39}{40}$
$\frac{1}{80}$	$\frac{79}{80}$

The children should notice that each time water is added, the 'whole' can be thought of as split into twice as many equal parts, one part of which will be blackcurrant.

Solutions:

1. (a) $\frac{1}{5}$ **(b)** $\frac{4}{5}$

2. (a) $\frac{1}{10}$ **(b)** $\frac{9}{10}$

3. (a) $\frac{1}{20}$ **(b)** $\frac{19}{20}$

4. The denominator will keep doubling and there will always be one part blackcurrant.

5. You will always have one part blackcurrant no matter how many times you do this, but the amount of blackcurrant will reduce by half each time.

6. 10

The pattern for the extension activity looks like this:

Blackcurrant	Water
$\frac{1}{4}$	$\frac{3}{4}$
$\frac{1}{8}$	$\frac{7}{8}$
$\frac{1}{16}$	$\frac{15}{16}$

Suggested questions:

● What do you notice about the fractions?
● Can you explain what the pattern is?
● After how many steps will less than $\frac{1}{1000}$ of the drink be blackcurrant?

Counter acts (page 17)

☆ *Processes: look for pattern, generalise, be systematic, predict, visualise, reason, record, explain, test ideas*

Solutions:

3	✗	✗	✔
4	✔	✔	✗
5	✗	✗	✗
6	✗	✔	✔
7	✗	✗	✗
8	✗	✔	✗
9	✔	✔	✗
10	✗	✔	✔
11	✗	✗	✗
12	✗	✔	✗
13	✗	✗	✗

14	✗	✓	✗
15	✗	✓	✓
16	✓	✓	✗
17	✗	✗	✗
18	✗	✓	✗

The children may notice the following patterns:

- The pattern of numbers that can be made into squares (known as square numbers) is 4 (2 × 2), 9 (3 × 3), 16 (4 × 4), and continues with 25 (5 × 5), 36 (6 × 6), and so on. The children may notice that between the first two square numbers there are four other numbers, and between the next two square numbers there are six numbers; the pattern continues, so that there are eight between the next two square numbers, and so on. Alternatively, the children could be asked to find the difference between adjacent square numbers (9 − 4 = 5, 16 − 9 = 7...) and they may notice that the differences are odd numbers.

- All numbers except prime numbers can be made into rectangles, although the children are unlikely to be familiar with the term and idea of primes. They are more likely to notice that all even numbers make rectangles, as well as other odd tables fact answers such as 9 (3 × 3) and 15 (3 × 5).

- The pattern of triangular numbers goes 3, 6, 10, 15..., the difference between adjacent numbers being 3, 4, 5, and so on. The next few numbers therefore are 21, 28, 36... The children are most likely to notice that there are two numbers, then three numbers, then four numbers between the ticks in this column.

Encourage the children to continue to predict and explore other numbers to test the patterns they have noticed.

Ask the children to observe also which numbers can be arranged to make none, some or all of the shapes: for example, 7 cannot be made into any of the shapes, whilst, if the patterns are continued, it will be found that 36 can be arranged into a square, different rectangles and a triangle.

Suggested questions:
- Can you tell us about the patterns you have found?
- Why do you think this happens?

Cats and dogs (page 18)
☆ *Processes: be systematic, reason, look for pattern, co-operate, explain*

This activity explores ideas of equivalent ratios in the context of cats and dogs.

Solutions:

2. (a) 4 : 2, 6 : 3, 8 : 4
  (b) 2 : 6, 3 : 9
  (c) 4 : 2, 5 : 3, 6 : 4, 7 : 5

Solutions to the extension activity:

3 : 3, 4 : 4, 5 : 5, 6 : 6
4 : 2, 6 : 3, 8 : 4
2 : 4, 3 : 6, 4 : 8
2 : 6, 3 : 9
6 : 2, 9 : 3
1 : 5, 2 : 10
5 : 1, 10 : 2

Suggested questions:
- How can you tell that two ratios are equivalent?
- Can you use the patterns to give another ratio that is equivalent to 2 : 4?

Haunted hotel (page 19)
☆ *Processes: simplify, be systematic, record, generalise, look for pattern, explain*

Some children may have limited recording skills and may need additional help. They could be encouraged to write all the numbers to 40 and then could write O or S (open or shut) next to each door as they are opened or closed.

After the 40 visits from the ghosts, the only doors left open will be square numbers, i.e. doors 1, 4, 9, 16, 25 and 36. The reason for this is that square numbers always have an odd number of factors (for example, 25 has the factors 1, 5 and 25), and other (non-square) numbers have an even number of factors. Therefore, when the ghosts are visiting the doors there will always be an odd number of visits to the square number doors, which leaves them open.

Suggested questions/prompts:
- What do you notice? Explain your thinking to your partner.
- What strategies did you use?

Chinese roots (page 20)
☆ *Processes: estimate, check, test ideas, predict, reason, compare, generalise*

The rules work for all square numbers and provide quite close results for other numbers, usually giving an answer less than two-tenths different from the true root. The larger the number, the closer the estimate will be.

The children could explore the reasons behind this method by considering the differences between the square numbers, for example:

$$+1 \qquad +3 \qquad +5 \qquad +7 \qquad +9$$
$$1 \qquad 4 \qquad 9 \qquad 16 \qquad 25$$

This pattern is the key to describing how the whole number digit of the root is found. The decimal part of the estimate is the approximation.

Suggested questions:
- Why do you think this happens?
- How close is this estimate?
- What other rules could we try?
- How could you improve on the rule?

Calculations

Crafty columns (page 21)
☆ *Processes: look for pattern, be systematic, reason, trial and improvement, compare, co-operate, check, generalise*

Possible solutions:

$c_5 + c_4 = c_1$ $c_4 + c_6 = c_2$
$c_3 + c_6 = c_1$ $c_3 + c_7 = c_2$
$c_2 + c_7 = c_1$ $c_2 + c_8 = c_2$
$c_1 + c_8 = c_1$ $c_1 + c_1 = c_2$

c5 + c6 = c3	c5 + c7 = c4
c4 + c7 = c3	c4 + c8 = c4
c3 + c8 = c3	c3 + c1 = c4
c2 + c1 = c3	c2 + c2 = c4
c6 + c7 = c5	c6 + c8 = c6
c5 + c8 = c5	c5 + c1 = c6
c4 + c1 = c5	c4 + c2 = c6
c3 + c2 = c5	c3 + c3 = c6
c7 + c8 = c7	c7 + c1 = c8
c6 + c1 = c7	c6 + c2 = c8
c5 + c2 = c7	c5 + c3 = c8
c4 + c3 = c7	c4 + c4 = c8

C8 added to any column leaves it unchanged.

Suggested questions:
- What have you found out?
- How can you be sure that you have found all the ways?
- Does this always work? Why?

Domino magic! (page 22)
☆ *Processes: reason, generalise, test ideas, look for pattern, explain, compare, ask own questions, simplify*

This activity can lead to some interesting generalisations and more confident children could use algebra to explain the patterns. All three sets of instructions on the page lead to the simplified expression $10x + y$, where x is one number on the domino and y is the other. Since x is multiplied by 10, it will appear as the tens digit of the answer.

To show how this can be found for the first set of instructions:

$x \times 5 = 5x$
$5x + 6$
$2 \times (5x + 6) = 10x + 12$
$10x + 12 + y$
$10x + 12 + y - 12 = 10x + y$

Suggested questions/prompts:
- What do you notice? Explain your thinking to your partner.
- How could you use what you have found to make other sets of instructions that do this?

Tennis teaser (page 23)
☆ *Processes: trial and improvement, reason, test ideas, predict*

There are many solutions to this puzzle. What is important is that the values relate to each other correctly.

Possible solution:

Ali = 50
Bev = 18
Caz = 32
Dan = 29

There are many possible solutions to the extension activity, for example:

A = 24, B = 19, C = 42, D = 49

Suggested questions:
- What did you notice?
- How did you work out the answers? What strategies did you use?
- Can you explain to the class what you did?

Party invitations (page 24)
☆ *Processes: reason, be systematic, look for pattern, explain, test ideas, check*

Solutions (the children may find other ways, but these are the fewest numbers of packs possible):

1. 68 invitations:
   2 packs of 6, 4 packs of 9 and 1 pack of 20 =
   7 packs altogether
2. 73 invitations:
   1 pack of 6, 3 packs of 9 and 2 packs of 20 =
   6 packs altogether
3. 99 invitations:
   2 packs of 6, 3 packs of 9 and 3 packs of 20 =
   8 packs altogether

Suggested questions:
- What strategies did you use?
- Where did you start?
- How easy did you find this?

Card shuffle: 1 and 2 (pages 25–26)
☆ *Processes: trial and improvement, reason, compare, record, make decisions, check*

There are many different solutions to this investigation, particularly if children are encouraged to seek out their own patterns and set their own criteria for arrangement. The following solutions involve totals of 36 for rows and columns, and no two numbers are the same in a row or a column.

The solution below has three red cards and three black cards in each row and column.

3 ◇	5 ◇	10 ◇	8 ♣	4 ♣	6 ♣
6 ♠	8 ♠	4 ♠	2 ♡	7 ♡	9 ♡
8 ◇	4 ◇	6 ◇	7 ♣	9 ♣	2 ♣
2 ♠	7 ♠	9 ♠	10 ♡	3 ♡	5 ♡
7 ◇	9 ◇	2 ◇	3 ♣	5 ♣	10 ♣
10 ♠	3 ♠	5 ♠	6 ♡	8 ♡	4 ♡

The solution below has three rows of red cards and three rows of black cards.

3 ◇	5 ◇	10 ◇	8 ◇	4 ◇	6 ◇
6 ♡	8 ♡	4 ♡	2 ♡	7 ♡	9 ♡
2 ◇	7 ◇	9 ◇	10 ♡	3 ♡	5 ♡
8 ♣	4 ♣	6 ♣	7 ♣	9 ♣	2 ♣
7 ♠	9 ♠	2 ♠	3 ♣	5 ♣	10 ♣
10 ♠	3 ♠	5 ♠	6 ♠	8 ♠	4 ♠

Suggested questions/prompts:
- Can you swap any cards around so that you get a line of red cards?
- Explain what you decided to do, and why.

Solving problems

Spellbound (page 27)

☆ *Processes: be systematic, look for pattern, visualise, generalise, simplify, check*

Solutions:

There are 12 ways to spell TEA and EAT, and 36 ways of spelling ATE.

There are 24 ways to spell TEAM, 12 ways to spell MEAT, and 72 ways of spelling MATE.

Other words that could be explored in a similar way include: RAM, ARM, MAR; TIDE, DIET, TIED.

Suggested questions:

● How many ways did you find?

● How can you be sure that you have found all the ways?

How much are you worth? (page 28)

☆ *Processes: make decisions, co-operate, test ideas, reason, record, explain*

Allow the children to make their own group decisions about how to find an answer to this question, and to choose appropriate ways of representing the information to others at the end. Be sensitive to the issue of weight for some children. If necessary, the children can be told that a £1 coin weighs exactly 9·8 g. In this case, allow the children to use a calculator to help solve the problem.

Suggested questions:

● How well did your group work together?

● What went well? What problems did you have?

● If you were going to do this again, what changes would you make?

Always, sometimes, never (page 29)

☆ *Processes: reason, visualise, explain, co-operate, test ideas, generalise*

Solutions:

1. Always true
2. Sometimes true (not true if cut along the diagonal)
3. Sometimes true (true for questions such as 0.2×5)
4. Sometimes true (not true for some decimals $\times 5$)
5. Never true
6. Always true (because $n - 1 + n + n + 1 = 3n$)

Suggested questions:

● In what situations is this statement not true?

● When is this statement true?

● How can you be sure?

● What if the number is a decimal?

● What about zero?

The Wizard of Odd (page 30)

☆ *Processes: be systematic, reason, look for pattern, record, check*

There are 20 combinations for the main activity:

ABC	ABD	ABE	ABF
	ACD	ACE	ACF
		ADE	ADF
			AEF

BCD	BCE	BCF
	BDE	BDF
		BEF
CDE	CDF	
	CEF	
	DEF	

Note that each combination could be written in a different order (for example, BCD could be written as BDC, CDB, CBD, DBC or DCB). Each child is included in 10 answers.

There are 15 combinations for the extension activity:

ABCD	ABCE	ABCF
	ABDE	ABDF
		ABEF
	ACDE	ACDF
		ACEF
		ADEF
BCDE	BCDF	BCEF
		BDEF
	CDEF	

Again, the letters can be written in any order.

Suggested questions:

● What have you discovered?

● How can you be sure that you have found all the combinations?

● Did you sort them in a particular way?

● How could you check?

Football tables (page 31)

☆ *Processes: test ideas, generalise, look for pattern, reason, be systematic*

Solutions:

1. A against B – A won
   C against D – draw

2.

A	3		B	3		C	3
C	1		C	1		A	1
D	1		D	1		B	1
B	0		A	0		D	0

D	3		A	3		B	3
A	1		D	3		C	3
B	1		B	0		A	0
C	0		C	0		D	0

B	3		A	3		A	1
D	3		C	3		B	1
A	0		B	0		C	1
C	0		D	0		D	1

3. 4 (first in two tables and equal first in two tables)

In the extension activity, teams B and C must win if C is to win the tournament.

Suggested questions:

● What other questions could you ask?

● How can you be sure that you have found all the ways?

You've been cubed! (page 32)

☆ *Processes: reason, simplify, visualise, look for pattern, explain, co-operate, test ideas, generalise*

This activity is based on a version of the ancient game Nim. Encourage the children to explore this game further by changing the lengths of the rows.

Ensure the children understand that they can only take cubes from one row at a time. Point out also that it does not matter which cubes are taken from a row.

The children should begin to notice, after they have played the game several times, that they should aim to leave two cubes in each of two rows at the end of their go. From this position they can definitely win. They should also look at the strategies necessary to get them into this winning position: for example, if there are cubes in three rows they may have to reduce them to two rows to get into the winning position.

Suggested questions:

- What patterns did you notice?
- What strategies did you use?
- Would you rather play first or second? Why?
- What happens if we change the length of each row?
- Which numbers of cubes are best to leave near the end?

Handling data

Average cards (page 33)

☆ *Processes: reason, explain, estimate*

The first four questions on the sheet provide the children with an opportunity to explore how missing numbers can be found.

Solutions:

1. **(a)** For the median to be 5, one of the missing numbers must be 5, and the other must be 5 or less.
   (b) For the range to be 8, one of the two missing numbers must be 9. The other could be any number.
   (c) For the mode to be 1, both of the missing numbers must be 1. If only one of the numbers were 1, then 1 and 6 would be modes.
   (d) For the mean to be 5, the two missing numbers must have a total of 12 (for example, 5 and 7 or 9 and 3).

2. It is impossible for the mean to be 3 (unless negative numbers are used), since the total already is 28. The total of all eight numbers would have to be 24 for the mean to be 3.

3. It is not possible for 7 to be the only mode, since only two cards can be 7 and therefore 6 would be a mode too.

4. It is possible for the median to be 5·5 if one missing number is 6 or higher and the other is 5 or less.

5. It is impossible for the range to be 6, since the range of the six numbers already shown is 7.

Suggested questions:

- How did you find the answers?
- How did estimating help?

Measures, shape and space

Digital light bars (page 34)

☆ *Processes: look for pattern, be systematic, predict, visualise, record, reason, compare, test ideas, simplify*

The time that uses the fewest bars is 11:11 (8 bars). The time that uses the most is 08:08 (26 bars). The number of light bars for other times varies between 8 and 26.

Once the children have begun to explore the number of light bars in each digit, they can then work more abstractly, choosing combinations of digits that have a particular total.

The number of light bars for each digit is as follows:

1 → 2 light bars
2 → 5 light bars
3 → 5 light bars
4 → 4 light bars
5 → 5 light bars
6 → 6 light bars
7 → 3 light bars
8 → 7 light bars
9 → 6 light bars
0 → 6 light bars

For the extension activity, the following are examples of times that use 15 light bars:

17:46 17:49 17:04 17:23 11:56 11:50 11:59 11:05
11:26 11:29 11:20 11:02 11:30 11:03 11:36 11:39
10:15 10:51 19:15 19:51 01:15 01:51 05:11 15:01
15:10 15:19

Suggested questions:

- Is this a real time?
- Would you see this time on a 24-hour clock?
- How many other real times could you make using these digits?

Stick insects (page 35)

☆ *Processes: estimate, co-operate, predict, record, test ideas, check*

Estimating is a valuable using and applying skill. This activity encourages children to estimate lengths to the nearest millimetre: for example, 44 mm; 4 cm and 4 mm; or even 4·4 cm.

Suggested question:

- What strategies did you use to improve your estimates?

Curious co-ordinates: 1 and 2
(pages 36–37)

☆ *Processes: visualise, test ideas, look for pattern, compare*

This activity allows the children to explore simple ideas of shears, where shapes are transformed by moving or changing the co-ordinate axes in different ways. Encourage the children to make their own sets of axes with numbers from 0 to 10 on each axis.

Suggested questions:

- What patterns did you find? What do you think your picture will look like on this grid?

What's your angle? (page 38)

☆ *Processes: test ideas, generalise, predict, compare, look for pattern*

The children should discover that for any circle, with any point marked on its circumference, the angle at the cross will be a right angle. Point out that the triangle formed by the diameter and the two lines joining it to the edge of the circle is a right-angled triangle.

Suggested questions:

- What did you notice?
- Do you think this is true for all triangles drawn on all circles, where the diameter is one side of the triangle?

Shape shuffle: 1 and 2 (pages 39–40)

☆ *Processes: record, visualise, compare, be systematic, trial and improvement*

Encourage the children to be systematic when joining the shapes to make new shapes (for example, by keeping one shape in the same position and moving the other to another side).

Solutions for two shapes:

triangle + triangle → rhombus

trapezium + trapezium → hexagons (including regular hexagon), parallelogram, pentagon, octagon

rhombus + rhombus → parallelogram, hexagon

triangle + trapezium → parallelogram, equilateral triangle, heptagon, hexagon

triangle + rhombus → trapezium

trapezium + rhombus → trapezium, pentagons, hexagon, heptagon, octagon

Solutions for three shapes:

triangle + triangle + triangle → trapezium

triangle + triangle + trapezium → trapezium, pentagon, hexagon, heptagons

triangle + triangle + rhombus → parallelogram, hexagon, equilateral triangle

trapezium + trapezium + triangle → trapezium, pentagons, hexagons, heptagons, octagons

***trapezium + trapezium + rhombus** → parallelogram, trapeziums, rhombus, pentagon, heptagons, octagons, nonagon, decagon, dodecagons ***

rhombus + rhombus + rhombus → parallelogram, hexagons, heptagons, octagons

rhombus + rhombus + triangle → trapeziums, pentagons, hexagons, heptagons

rhombus + rhombus + trapezium → trapeziums, pentagon, hexagons, heptagons, octagons, decagon

triangle + trapezium + rhombus → parallelogram, pentagon, hexagons, heptagons, octagons

*** two trapeziums and a rhombus can be arranged to make both a parallelogram and a trapezium.

Suggested question:

- How could you make an equilateral triangle using two or three shapes?

Grow-Faster Granules (page 41)

☆ *Processes: simplify, reason, explain, co-operate, record, test ideas, make decisions*

Ensure the children understand the principle of mixing fertiliser granules with water, and sprinkling it on an area of lawn. They should find that $40\,m^2$ of lawn can be covered by the fertiliser mixture.

Encourage the children to work together and to discuss their decisions about how to solve this problem. It is important that they try the extension activity, so that they learn to communicate their ideas clearly on paper.

Suggested questions:

- How did you work this out?
- Can you explain what you did?

Vertex variations (page 42)

☆ *Processes: visualise, look for pattern, reason, be systematic, compare, test ideas*

It may be helpful to demonstrate this idea on a computer, although this is not necessary.

Solutions:

A square can be changed into kites and arrowhead kites, a right-angled triangle, trapeziums and quadrilaterals.

The trapezium can be changed into a square, a kite, an arrowhead kite, a right-angled triangle and different trapeziums.

Suggested questions:

- Have you found all the shapes it could be changed into? How can you be sure?

Time travel (page 43)

☆ *Processes: trial and improvement, make decisions, estimate, be systematic, compare, test ideas, check*

Encourage the children to describe any strategies that they used for this activity. These could include strategies such as going through the 1-hour pad in the fourth row, rather than the 3-hour pad, to ensure a smaller total. However, this may not prove to be the best strategy, as many of the pads around the 1-hour pad have large numbers of minutes. Encourage the children to record different routes and their total times.

Solutions:

The shortest route is 4 hours and 25 minutes, which starts on the second pad in the top row and goes down the left-hand side of the board. The route for the extension activity is: 45 minutes, 15 minutes, 15 minutes, 45 minutes, 1 hour, 50 minutes, 40 minutes, 25 minutes, 5 minutes.

Suggested questions:

- What strategies did you use?
- How did you start off? Did you just try any route?
- Next time, what could you do to improve your strategy?

Crazy co-ordinates (page 44)

☆ *Processes: look for pattern, be systematic, visualise, reason, explain*

Encourage the children to explore the symmetries of the patterns using mirrors, and to explain what they notice. When finding all the possible sets of co-ordinates, note that if two digits are the same there will be six sets, and if all the digits are different there will be 12 sets. Encourage a systematic approach and discuss any strategies that the children used to find all the different sets.

If the children are not yet experienced in drawing and labelling their own co-ordinate grids, mask the digits in the shaded boxes and the worked example, and copy this version of the sheet for the children to use when carrying out the extension activity.

Solutions:

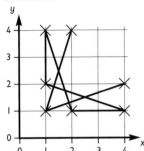 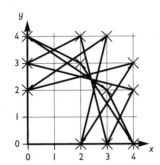

Further investigation can lead the children to discover that sometimes two lines join up to form a straight line: for example, if the digits 1, 2, 3 and 4 are used, the co-ordinates (1, 4) and (3, 2) form a straight line with (4, 1) and (2, 3).

Each set of digits forms a different pattern on the grid. These can all be drawn and displayed to stimulate further discussion and interest.

Suggested questions:
● What do you notice?
● How are these two patterns similar?
● Is the pattern symmetrical?
● What strategies did you use to find all the sets of co-ordinates?
● What if we tried three or four digits the same?

Talking angles (page 45)
☆ Processes: explain, co-operate, compare, visualise, estimate

This activity focuses attention on describing angles accurately and explaining their orientation. Encourage the children to use specific language, such as the words in the box on the activity sheet.

Suggested questions:
● In what way is this card different from this one?
● How could you describe this card?
● What key words did you need to use in order to describe the angles accurately?

Mass hysteria (page 46)
☆ Processes: estimate, co-operate, predict, record, test ideas, check

This activity encourages children to estimate masses of small items. At the start of the lesson you will need a collection of the items listed on the sheet and a suitable set of kitchen scales (ideally an electronic set). If you do not have some of the items on the sheet, then the sheet can be altered before copying.

Suggested questions:
● How good were your estimates?
● Did you get better each time you estimated?

Peas, please (page 47)
☆ Processes: reason, co-operate, predict, test ideas, compare, record, estimate, explain, generalise

The concept of capacity could be discussed in relation to this investigation. The following are the actual capacities of the containers that can be made. Of course, the children's answers will be given as numbers of dried peas, but they should produce results in the same order of size.

Solutions:

Dimensions of rectangle	Container A	Container B
1 cm × 36 cm	103 cm^3	2·9 cm^3
2 cm × 18 cm	51·6 cm^3	5·7 cm^3
3 cm × 12 cm	34·4 cm^3	8·5 cm^3
4 cm × 9 cm	25·8 cm^3	11·5 cm^3
6 cm × 6 cm	17·2 cm^3	17·2 cm^3

The shorter, wider containers have the largest capacities.

Squares of card will provide two identical containers.

As a further investigation, the children could look at the perimeters of the rectangles of card: for example, choosing rectangles with the same perimeters and seeing whether the capacities of the containers created are the same. They should discover that the greater the perimeter of the rectangle, the greater the capacity of the short, wide containers created.

More confident children could also explore how much card would be necessary to create a closed cylinder, such as a food tin, and then discuss why food tins are the shape that they are.

Suggested questions:
● What have you noticed about the number of peas that the short, wide containers hold?
● What about the tall, thin containers?
● What is special about the containers made from squares of card?

Troublesome triangles (page 48)
☆ Processes: simplify, visualise, be systematic, look for pattern, record, compare, check

To complete this activity, the children will need to simplify the diagrams into the different-sized and different-shaped triangles. Encourage them to work systematically and to record their solutions in a way which is easy to understand.

Solutions:

1. 8   **2.** 9
3. 12   **4.** 13

Suggested questions:
● How did you decide to record the triangles?
● How many have you found?
● How do you know you have found them all?

Square houses

- **Find the** square **of each roof number. Write it on the house.**

- **Can you add** three **square numbers to give an answer that is a square number? Find as many solutions as you can.**

- **Now add** two **square numbers to make another square number. Record your solutions on the back of this sheet.**

Now try this!

- **Look at your solutions for adding three numbers. Write out the roof numbers, like this: 1 2 2 3**
- **Use any patterns you notice to find more solutions.**

Teachers' note This investigation can be extended beyond the twelfth square number, to include all other three-digit square numbers. This will allow opportunities for the children to see patterns, make predictions and test larger numbers (see page 7). If appropriate, work on the two square numbers that make a third can be discussed in the context of right-angled triangles (in which the squares of the two shorter sides make the square of the longest side of the triangle).

Developing Numeracy
Using & Applying Maths
Year 6
© A & C BLACK

Steep signs

You need five long strips of thin card.

You are going to make ramps to match these road signs.

- **Tick the ramp which you think will be the steepest.**

  Put a cross by the one you think will be the least steep.

   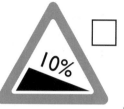 

- **Make a ramp to match this road sign.**

☆ Fold one of your strips in half to find the halfway point.

☆ Use a ruler to divide the left half into five equal parts.

☆ Fold the left side of the strip as shown below. Then fold the strip on the halfway point to complete the ramp.

The gradient of this ramp is **1 : 4**. For every one you go up, you go across four.

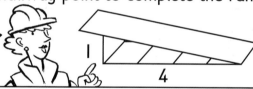

- **Now make ramps to match the other road signs.**

  For 1 : 8, divide the left-hand half into nine equal parts.
  For 20%, divide the left-hand half into six equal parts.
  For 1 : 7, divide the left-hand half into eight equal parts.
  For 10%, divide the left-hand half into eleven equal parts.

- **How accurate were your predictions?**

 Now try this!

- **Write the signs in order, from least steep to steepest.**
- **Make up five signs of your own. Write these in the correct places on your list.**

Teachers' note Discuss that a gradient of 10% is equivalent to a gradient of 1 : 10. Explain that on a 1 : 10 slope, you travel 10 units across for every 1 unit travelled up or down. Whilst some children may have an understanding of ratio and percentage notation, it is beneficial to consolidate this understanding by making the ramps practically. For this the children will need five strips of thin card and a ruler.

**Developing Numeracy
Using & Applying Maths
Year 6
© A & C BLACK**

Diluting dilemma

Visualise and explain

- **Imagine you are following these instructions.**

Step 1 Put blackcurrant cordial and water into a glass so that $\frac{1}{5}$ is blackcurrant and $\frac{4}{5}$ is water.

Step 2 Mix the drink well.

Step 3 Drink half of the mixture.

Step 4 Fill the glass to the top with water and mix it.

Step 5 Drink half of the mixture.

Step 6 Fill the glass to the top with water and mix it.

Repeat the last two steps several times.

1. At the end of step 2, what fraction of the drink is:

   (a) blackcurrant? _____   **(b)** water? _____

2. At the end of step 4, what fraction of the drink is:

   (a) blackcurrant? _____   **(b)** water? _____

3. At the end of step 6, what fraction of the drink is:

   (a) blackcurrant? _____   **(b)** water? _____

4. What will happen if you keep following the last two steps? Tell a partner.

5. Will you ever have no blackcurrant? Explain your answer.

   _____

   _____

6. After how many steps would there be 79 times more water than

   blackcurrant? _____

- **Write an explanation of what would happen if $\frac{1}{4}$ of the drink was blackcurrant and $\frac{3}{4}$ was water.**

Teachers' note Some children may find this situation difficult to visualise and might benefit from a demonstration at the beginning of the lesson. Encourage the children to sketch their own diagrams to help them visualise the process and ensure they appreciate that, even though the parts are mixed, the fractions of water and blackcurrant do not change unless more water is added.

Developing Numeracy
Using & Applying Maths
Year 6
© A & C BLACK

Counter acts

Look for patterns and generalise

You need 18 counters, all the same size.

☆ Collect the number of counters shown in the first column.

☆ Can you arrange that number of counters to make any of the shapes shown? The counters must touch and you must not leave any large gaps in the middle of the shapes.

Number of counters to be arranged	Can you make a **square**?	Can you make a **rectangle** (including squares) with more than one row?	Can you make a **triangle**?
3	✗	✗	✔
4	✔	✔	
5			
6			
7			
8			
9			
10			
11			
12			
13			
14			
15			
16			
17			
18			

Now try this!

- **Describe to a partner any patterns you notice.**
- **Predict what will happen for other numbers of counters up to 30.**
- **Test your predictions.** You need 30 counters.

Teachers' note Ensure the children understand that they must use all the counters shown in the left-hand column. As they work systematically down the list, the children should begin to notice some patterns. Encourage them to describe these in their own words and to use the patterns to make predictions about other numbers. To focus on explanations, the children could be asked to write a page of a maths book to explain these patterns to another child of their own age.

**Developing Numeracy
Using & Applying Maths
Year 6
© A & C BLACK**

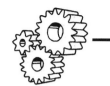

Cats and dogs

Be systematic and reason

Claws and Paws is a pet hotel for cats and dogs. In the hotel there are from ⬚6⬚ to ⬚12⬚ pets at any time.

There must be at least one of each pet.

1. Write all the possible **ratios** of cats to dogs.

6	7	8	9	10	11	12
cats : dogs	cats : dogs	cats : dogs	cats : dogs	cats : dogs	cats : dogs	cats : dogs
1 : 5	1 : 6	1 : 7	1 : 8	1 : 9	1 : 10	1 : 11
2 : 4	2 : 5	:	:	:	:	:
3 : 3	:	:	:	:	:	:
:	:	:	:	:	:	:
:	:	:	:	:	:	:
	:	:	:	:	:	:
		:	:	:	:	:
			:	:	:	:
				:	:	:
					:	:
						:

2. With a partner, find all the ratios where there are:

(a) twice as many cats as dogs _____

(b) three times as many dogs as cats _____

(c) exactly two more cats than dogs _____

3. Talk about any patterns you see in your answers.

Now try this!

- **List sets of ratios which show the same ratio of cats to dogs.** Example: 4 : 2, 6 : 3 ...

Teachers' note Ensure the children understand that the first number in each ratio shows the number of cats and the second number shows the number of dogs. For the extension activity, the children could use different-coloured pencils to mark the sets of ratios in the lists on the sheet. This will enable them to see more patterns and to appreciate why some ratios that look different stand for the same (for example, 3 : 3 shows the cats and dogs in the same ratio as 4 : 4).

**Developing Numeracy
Using & Applying Maths
Year 6
© A & C BLACK**

Haunted hotel

Simplify, be systematic and record information

- ## Read the following description.

The hotel rooms are numbered 1 to 40. All the doors are shut.

Ghost 1 walks from room to room in order. He goes to every door, starting with 1, and opens them.

Then Ghost 2 walks from room to room in order. She goes to every second door, starting with 2, and shuts them.

Ghost 3 follows behind. He goes to every third door, starting with 3. If the door is open he shuts it; if the door is shut he opens it.

Ghost 4 follows behind. She goes to every fourth door, starting with 4. If the door is open she shuts it; if the door is shut she opens it.

Ghost 5 follows behind. He goes to every fifth door, starting with 5. If the door is open he shuts it; if the door is shut he opens it.

Ghost 6 follows behind. She goes to every sixth door…

- ## If the pattern continues in the same way, which doors will be open after the 40th ghost has walked along the corridors?

Show your workings on a separate piece of paper.

Now try this!

- ## Explain what is special about the doors that are open.

_____

- ## Suggest the reason why this happens.

_____

_____

_____

Teachers' note Encourage the children to develop their own methods of recording; however, an effective recording strategy is vital for this exercise and some children may require additional guidance. See page 8 for more information. The children will benefit from understanding factors in order to explain the results of the extension activity.

**Developing Numeracy
Using & Applying Maths
Year 6
© A & C BLACK**

Chinese roots

Make estimates, check, and test your ideas

It is easy to find the square root $\boxed{\sqrt{}}$ **of a square number.**

Here are the square numbers:

| 1 | 4 | 9 | 16 | 25 | 36 | 49 | 64 | 81 | 100... |

Here are some of the square roots:

$\sqrt{16} = 4$ $\sqrt{25} = 5$ $\sqrt{81} = 9$ $\sqrt{100} = 10$

> But how can I find the square root of non-square numbers?

Before calculators, Chinese mathematicians discovered a way of finding an **approximate** square root.

Rules

☆ Write the number you want to find the square root of.   **32**

☆ Subtract 1, then 3, then 5, then 7, then 9…, until you cannot subtract the next odd number.

−1, 31
−3, 28

☆ Count how many odd numbers you have subtracted. Here it is **5**.

−5, 23
−7, 16

☆ Look at the remainder. Here it is **7**.

−9, 7

☆ The approximate square root of 32 is **5·7**.

$\sqrt{32}$ **is about 5·7**

- **Choose non-square numbers less than 50. Use the rules to find the <u>approximate</u> square root of each number.**

- **Now find the <u>actual</u> square roots. How close were your estimates?**

> **You need a calculator.**

Teachers' note At the start of the lesson, ensure that the children understand square numbers, and discuss what the square root of a number is (for example, finding the square root of 32 means finding which number, when multiplied by itself, gives 32). Stress that the Chinese method only provides approximate answers and, as an extension, encourage the children to make adaptations to the rules to improve the estimates, ensuring that their adaptation works for all number ranges.

**Developing Numeracy
Using & Applying Maths
Year 6**
© A & C BLACK

Crafty columns

Look for patterns

The numbers in this grid are arranged in rows of 8.

- **Follow these instructions.**

☆ Choose any number in column 4 (c4) and any number in column 7 (c7). Add them together.

☆ If the answer is in the grid, shade it red.

☆ Try this several times. What do you notice?

c4 + c7 = c____

c4					c7		
1	2	3	4	5	6	7	8
9	10	11	12	13	14	15	16
17	18	19	20	21	22	23	24
25	26	27	28	29	30	31	32
33	34	35	36	37	38	39	40
41	42	43	44	45	46	47	48
49	50	51	52				
57							

☆ Now add together numbers from columns c6 and c3.

☆ Shade the answers blue. What do you notice?

c6 + c3 = c____

- **Investigate what happens when you add together numbers from other columns.**

c____ + c____ = c____

c____ + c____ = c____

c____ + c____ = c____

c____ + c____ = c____

c____ + c____ = c____

c____ + c____ = c____

c____ + c____ = c____

c____ + c____ = c____

c____ + c____ = c____

c____ + c____ = c____

c____ + c____ = c____

c____ + c____ = c____

c____ + c____ = c____

c____ + c____ = c____

c____ + c____ = c____

- **What is special about adding c8? Talk to a partner.**

- **On the back of this sheet, write all the different ways you can find to make c5.**

- **Investigate a different grid with 6, 7, 9 or 10 columns.**

You need squared paper.

Teachers' note Ensure that the children are familiar with the word 'column' and that they understand the instructions. When the children have been investigating for a while, compile a class list of results. Draw attention to the patterns and numbers of solutions for each column number. For the extension activity, encourage the children to compare their results.

Developing Numeracy
Using & Applying Maths
Year 6
© A & C BLACK

Domino magic!

Reason, generalise and test your ideas

Here is a full set of dominoes.
- ## Choose a domino and follow
  ## the instructions below.

☆ Multiply one of the numbers on your domino by 5.

☆ Add 6.

☆ Multiply by 2.

☆ Add the other number on your domino.

☆ Subtract 12.

The digits of your answer are the two numbers on your domino.

And that's magic!

- **Try this several times. What do you notice?**

_____

_____

- **With a partner, discuss why you think this happens.**

- **Which of these sets of instructions will do the same thing?**

☆ Multiply one of the numbers on your domino by 5.	☆ Multiply one of the numbers on your domino by 2.
☆ Add 10.	☆ Add 2.
☆ Multiply by 2.	☆ Multiply by 5.
☆ Add the other number on your domino.	☆ Add the other number on your domino.
☆ Subtract 20.	☆ Subtract 10.

- **Talk to a partner about why this is.**

- **Call one number on the domino x and the other y. Work through the first set of instructions. What do you notice? Then try the other two sets of instructions.**

Teachers' note Some children may find the extension activity a little difficult. If this is the case, work through it together as a class (see page 9 for more information). Once the children appreciate that one number becomes ten times larger to form the tens digit, they can create their own sets of instructions that have this effect.

Developing Numeracy
Using & Applying Maths
Year 6
© A & C BLACK

Tennis teaser

Four adults play tennis.

The adults are all different ages.

When Ali and Bev play each other, the total of their ages is 68.

When Caz and Dan play each other, the total of their ages is 61.

When Caz and Bev play each other, the total of their ages is 50.

When Ali and Dan play each other, the total of their ages is 79.

- **Who do you think is:** oldest? _____ youngest? _____

- **Work out the age of each person.**

Show your workings here.

Ali's age _____   Bev's age _____   Caz's age _____   Dan's age _____

- **Compare your answers with a partner's. Try to find more than one answer.**

Now try this!

- **Use the same strategy to find what A, B, C and D are, if:**

A + B = 43   C + D = 91

C + B = 61   D + A = 73

Teachers' note The children are likely to start by using trial and improvement strategies, such as choosing ages for each person and then checking whether those ages work. They should then be encouraged to modify these by altering numbers one at a time. Deciding which they think will be the oldest or youngest person can help them to modify their guesses more effectively.

Developing Numeracy
Using & Applying Maths
Year 6
© A & C BLACK

Party invitations

Invitation cards come in packs of 6, 9 and 20.

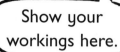

1. Imagine you are having a party and want to buy **exactly** 68 invitation cards.

   What is the fewest number of packs you can buy?

   Show your workings here.

2. What if you want to buy **exactly** 73 invitation cards?

   What is the fewest number of packs you can buy?

3. What if you want to buy **exactly** 99 invitation cards?

   What is the fewest number of packs you can buy?

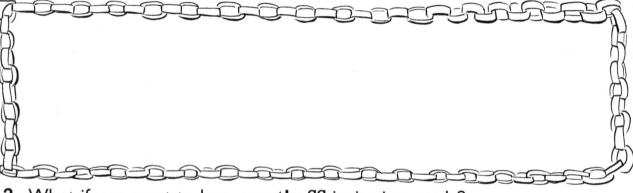

Now try this!

- **Make up your own invitation card problems for a partner to solve.**

  There must be only one answer to each problem.

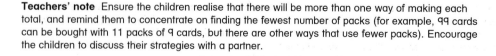

Teachers' note Ensure the children realise that there will be more than one way of making each total, and remind them to concentrate on finding the fewest number of packs (for example, 99 cards can be bought with 11 packs of 9 cards, but there are other ways that use fewer packs). Encourage the children to discuss their strategies with a partner.

Developing Numeracy
Using & Applying Maths
Year 6
© A & C BLACK

24

Card shuffle: 1

- **You need the cards from *Card shuffle: 2*.**

1. Arrange the cards in six rows of six, so that each row totals **36** and each column totals **36**. Record your arrangement below.

Don't forget to include ♥ ♦ ♣ ♠.

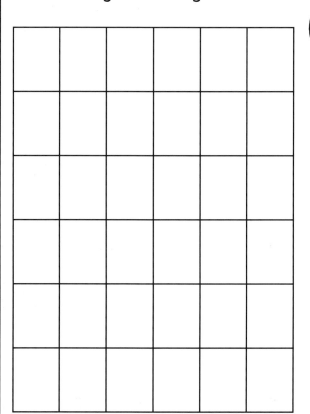

2. Swap cards around. Can you find a solution where the same number does not appear twice in the same row or column?

3. Is it possible to swap your cards around to make a row, column or diagonal that is all red?

yes ☐   no ☐

Now try this!

- **Arrange the cards in a pattern of your choice. Stick them onto a piece of paper.**

Make sure you have totals of **36** and patterns of red cards.

- **Write an explanation of the patterns.**

Teachers' note The children will need the cards from page 26 (or a pack of playing cards with aces and picture cards removed). Encourage them to use strategies of trial and improvement when tackling this problem: for example, 'This row comes to 37, so can I swap a card for one that is one less?' For the extension activity, encourage the children to choose their own arrangement, which could perhaps involve three red cards and three non-red cards in each row and column, or diagonal lines of red.

**Developing Numeracy
Using & Applying Maths
Year 6
© A & C BLACK**

Card shuffle: 2

• **Colour the hearts and diamonds red. Cut out the cards.**

2 ♡	3 ♡	4 ♡	5 ♡	6 ♡	7 ♡
8 ♡	9 ♡	10 ♡	2 ♠	3 ♠	4 ♠
5 ♠	6 ♠	7 ♠	8 ♠	9 ♠	10 ♠
2 ◇	3 ◇	4 ◇	5 ◇	6 ◇	7 ◇
8 ◇	9 ◇	10 ◇	2 ♣	3 ♣	4 ♣
5 ♣	6 ♣	7 ♣	8 ♣	9 ♣	10 ♣

Teachers' note These cards should be cut out and used with the activity on page 25.

**Developing Numeracy
Using & Applying Maths
Year 6
© A & C BLACK**

26

Spellbound

Be systematic and look for patterns

- **Start at** ⬜T **in the centre and follow the lines. How many different ways can you make the word** ⬜TEA **?** ⬜ **ways**

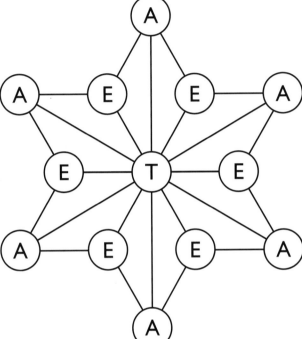

- **Find how many ways you can make the word** ⬜EAT **.**

  ⬜ **ways**

- **Find how many ways you can make the word** ⬜ATE **.**

  ⬜ **ways**

- **Talk to a partner about what you notice.**

- **On this diagram, how many different ways can you make these words?**

  TEAM ⬜ ways

  MEAT ⬜ ways

  MATE ⬜ ways

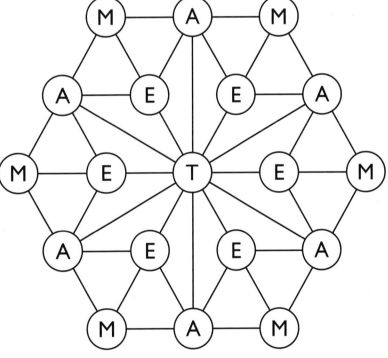

- **Make up your own spelling puzzle for a partner to investigate.**

Teachers' note This activity helps the children to develop systematic approaches to solving puzzles: working in an organised way; taking each option in turn; looking for pattern (such as noticing that, since there are patterns of 6 'spokes' on these diagrams, the total number of ways might be a multiple of 6). When the children design their own spelling puzzles, they should give thought to which words have letters that can be rearranged to make a new word. See page 10 for suggestions.

Developing Numeracy
Using & Applying Maths
Year 6
© A & C BLACK

How much are you worth?

Make decisions, co-operate and test your ideas

- **Work in a small group.**
  One of you needs to volunteer
  for the experiment.

Me! Me!

- **Discuss how you could find out**
  the answer to this question:

How many £1 coins weigh
the same as_____?

Fill in the name
of the volunteer.

- **Make a list of what you are going to do.**

How we plan to find out the information (who will do what?)

What resources we will need

- **Now follow your plan. Write what you find out.**

_____

_____

_____

Now try this!

Here are the masses of other British coins.

1p = 3·56 g	2p = 7·13 g	5p = 3·25 g
10p = 6·5 g	20p = 5 g	50p = 8 g

- **For each type of coin, find how much money weighs**
  the same as your volunteer.

Teachers' note This activity gives the children an opportunity to be in charge of their own planning and to make decisions about what to do. Discuss that some options may not be appropriate (such as weighing hundreds of pound coins!). Allow the children to use calculators, if necessary. They are also likely to need access to bathroom scales and kitchen scales, or those that can measure to the nearest 10g. See page 10 for information on the mass of a £1 coin.

Developing Numeracy
Using & Applying Maths
Year 6
© A & C BLACK

Always, sometimes, never

Reason and visualise

- **With a partner, talk about each of these statements. Write whether you think it is** | always true |, | sometimes true | **or** | never true |.

1.

The total of two whole numbers is a whole number.

2.

If I cut off a triangle from the corner of a square, I am left with a pentagon.

3.

When I multiply a decimal by a whole number, the answer is a whole number.

4.

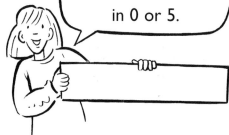

When I multiply a number by 5, the answer ends in 0 or 5.

5.

When a triangle is folded in half, it looks like a square.

6.

The total of three consecutive whole numbers is a multiple of 3.

- **Discuss your answers in a small group. Do you all agree?**

Now try this!

- **Write three statements to match each label:**

| always true | | sometimes true | | never true |

- **Give examples to prove your statements.**

Teachers' note This activity focuses on using reasoning to determine whether statements are always true, sometimes true or never true (and to consider, if appropriate, in what circumstances a statement is true). Encourage discussion of each situation in pairs and small groups, then as a whole class. Draw attention to the use of the word 'number' in the fourth statement and discuss whether this necessarily means only a whole number.

Developing Numeracy
Using & Applying Maths
Year 6
© A & C BLACK

The Wizard of Odd

Be systematic

In the school play, six children all want to be one of the three main characters: Here are the six children.

Timid Tiger *Metal Man* *Miss Hay*

Amber   Ben   Claire   Deepa   Emma   Felix

- **The teacher chooses three of them. Which three could they be? Use the first letters of their names to record the different combinations.**

Keep going until you are sure you have found all the combinations.

A B C   A B D   A B E

- **How many of your answers above include:**

  Amber? _____   Ben? _____   Claire? _____

  Deepa? _____   Emma? _____   Felix? _____

Now try this!

- **If <u>four</u> of the children were given parts in the school play, would there be more or fewer combinations? Find them all.**

  Example: ABCD ABCE

Teachers' note Ensure the children understand that the sex of the children and the order in which they are recorded are unimportant (for example, in the combination ABC the same children are chosen as in BCA, so this only needs to be recorded once). Encourage the children to persevere and to try to convince themselves that they have found all the combinations. See page 10 for solutions.

Developing Numeracy
Using & Applying Maths
Year 6
© A & C BLACK

Football tables

In a football tournament there are four teams: A, B, C and D.

APPLETON UNITED

BEECHESTER CITY

CECIL TOWN

DEEFORD ROVERS

The first two matches are   A against B   and   C against D.

The table shows the points after these two matches.

1. Write what must have happened
in each match.

A against B _____

C against D _____

A	3
C	1
D	1
B	0

Teams score
3 points for a win,
1 point for a draw,
0 points for a loss.

2. What different results could have happened in these two matches?
Fill in the tables to show all the other possible results.

3. The next match is <u>B against C</u>. It is a draw.

In how many of the tables above will B now be in first place? _____

Now try this!

With two matches to go, the table looks like this:

The last two matches are

B against D   **and**   A against C.

D	4
A	3
C	2
B	1

• **What results would mean that C win the**

tournament? _____

Teachers' note Ensure the children notice that the order of the teams in the table should change so that the team with the most points is at the top. If two teams have the same number of points, they should be written in alphabetical order.

**Developing Numeracy
Using & Applying Maths
Year 6
© A & C BLACK**

You've been cubed!

- **Play this game with a partner.**
- **Place 16 cubes on the squares below.**

You need
16 cubes.

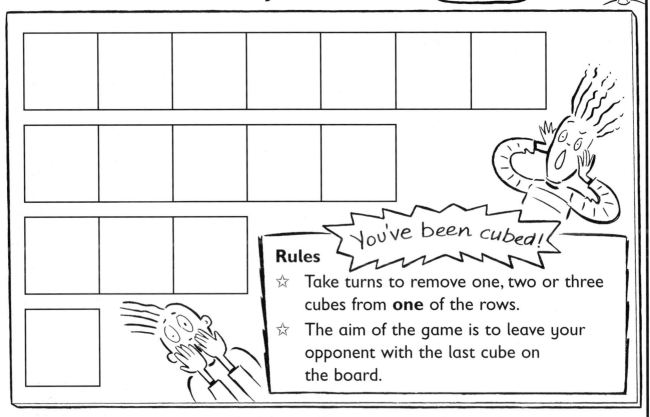

Rules

☆ Take turns to remove one, two or three cubes from **one** of the rows.

☆ The aim of the game is to leave your opponent with the last cube on the board.

You've been cubed!

- **Play the game several times. Can you work out how to win the game every time? Talk to your partner about your strategies and write some of them here.**

_____

_____

_____

_____

_____

Now try this!

- **Draw your own game board with rows of different lengths. Play using the same rules. How can you be sure to win? Is it best to go first or second?**

Teachers' note Each pair needs one copy of the sheet. To find winning strategies for this game, simplify it by considering shorter rows with fewer cubes and examining what a player must do for each situation. This can help the children to focus on the importance of leaving a particular number of cubes at the end of their go. Encourage the children to discuss and communicate their thinking to others, including explaining strategies on paper to form part of a display.

Developing Numeracy
Using & Applying Maths
Year 6
© A & C BLACK

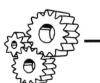

Average cards

Reason and explain

Here are eight cards which show any numbers from 1 to 9.

Some of the cards can show the same number.

Two cards are face down.

| 2 | | 8 | | 6 | 5 | 6 | 1 |

1. What could the two missing numbers be, if the:

    (a) median of the set was 5 _____

    (b) range of the set was 8 _____

    (c) mode of the set was 1 _____

    (d) mean of the set was 5 _____

• **Answer these questions. Explain your answers.**

2. Is it possible for the **mean** of the set to be 3?

_____

_____

3. Is it possible for the only **mode** of the set to be 7?

_____

_____

4. Is it possible for the **median** of the set to be 5·5?

_____

_____

5. Is it possible for the **range** of the set to be 6?

_____

_____

Now try this!

• **Draw your own set of cards with two missing numbers.**

• **Write four statements that are possible and four that are impossible. Write an explanation for each.**

Teachers' note Begin the lesson by discussing the meaning of the words 'mean', 'median', 'mode' and 'range'. Give examples, including those where the median lies between two middle numbers, and include situations where there is more than one mode. Encourage discussion in small groups or pairs to give children the opportunity to hear others' explanations. Some of the written explanations from this sheet could be used for display purposes.

**Developing Numeracy
Using & Applying Maths
Year 6
© A & C BLACK**

Digital light bars

Look for patterns and be systematic

A 24-hour digital clock has 28 light bars.

The time ⌈04:23⌉ uses 20 of these bars.

- Investigate other times that can be shown on a 24-hour clock. Write how many light bars they use.

Which time uses the most bars? Which uses the fewest bars?

- Which times on a 24-hour clock use exactly ⌈15⌉ light bars? Find as many as you can.

**Developing Numeracy
Using & Applying Maths
Year 6
© A & C BLACK**

Teachers' note It will be useful to have spare copies of the sheet available. Ensure that the children understand the idea of light bars on a digital clock. The children could work together to compile a list of which times use which numbers of light bars. Encourage them to explore the number of bars used for each digit and then to use this information to generate further results. Remind them that the times must be real times on a 24-hour clock, such as 02:34. See page 11 for more information.

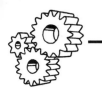

Stick insects

Make estimates and co-operate

- **Play this game with a partner.**

You need a ruler marked in millimetres.

☆ Take turns to choose a stick insect and **estimate** its length in millimetres.

☆ Your partner should measure the insect to check your estimate.

☆ If your estimate is within 5 mm of the actual length, score 3 points.

If your estimate is within 10 mm of the actual length, score 1 point.

☆ The winner is the player with the highest score at the end.

length

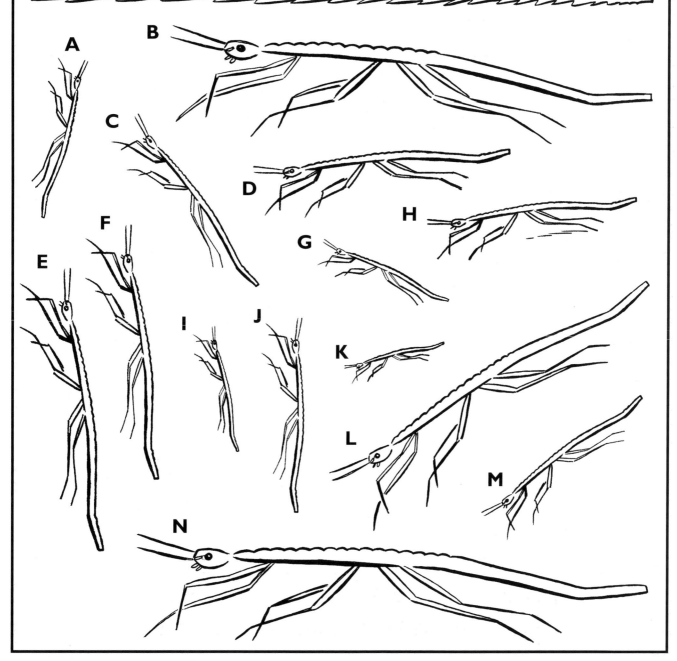

Teachers' note Each pair needs one copy of the sheet. Ask the children to record on scrap paper the letter of the insect, the estimate, the actual length and the difference in millimetres. Draw this in table form on the board for them to copy at the start of the lesson. To make a second sheet with insects of different lengths, the page could be reduced when photocopying (for example, to 96% or 84%). As an extension, the children could draw their own stick insects and play the game again.

Developing Numeracy
Using & Applying Maths
Year 6
© A & C BLACK

Curious co-ordinates: 1

Test your ideas and visualise

- On another piece of paper, write the co-ordinates of each vertex of the robot.

- Use the co-ordinates you have written to draw the robot on each grid.

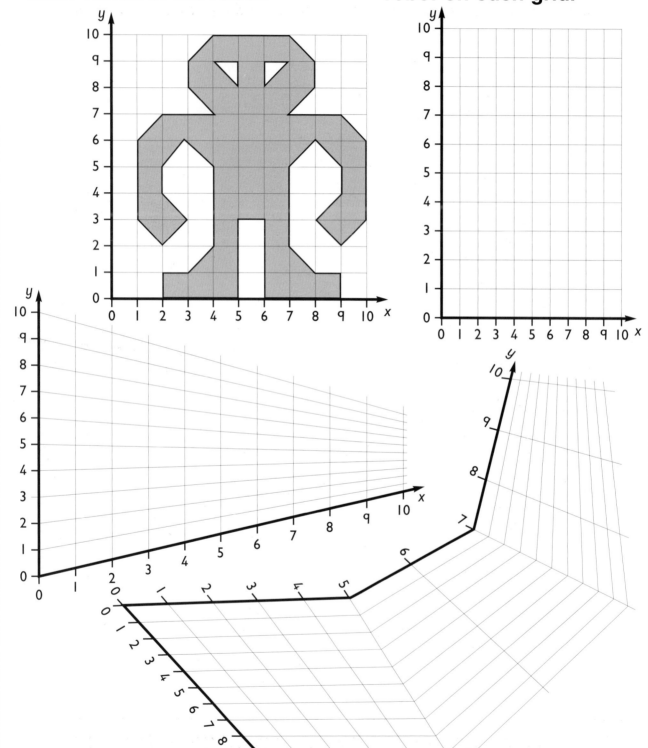

Teachers' note This page could be enlarged onto A3 paper to give larger grids if desired. If necessary, remind the children how to write and plot co-ordinates. Also ensure they understand the term 'vertex'. As an extension, the children could draw a co-ordinate grid on squared paper with numbers 0 to 10 on each axis, and then design their own picture to transform in different ways. Page 37 can be used for this purpose.

Developing Numeracy
Using & Applying Maths
Year 6
© A & C BLACK

☆ On squared paper, draw a grid with the numbers 0 to 10 on each axis.

You need
squared paper.

☆ Draw a picture on your grid. Write the co-ordinates of each vertex.

☆ Use the co-ordinates you have written to draw the picture on this grid.

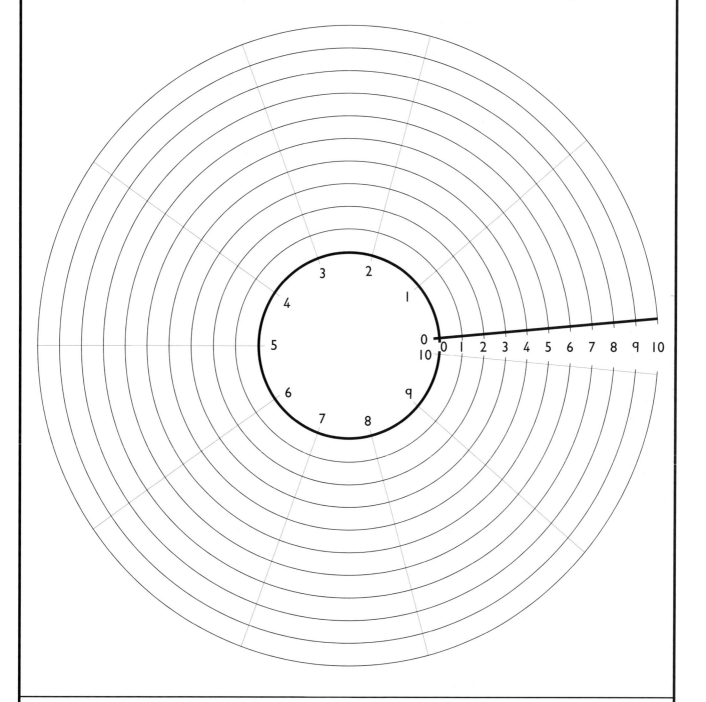

• **Draw your own different-shaped grids. Plot your picture on them.**

Teachers' note This sheet can be used to extend the activity on page 36. When drawing their own different-shaped grids, the children should start by drawing the x-axis and labelling it from 0 to 10. From each of these points another line, which could be curved or zigzag, should be drawn. The line leading from zero on the x-axis should be split into ten parts and labelled 0 to 10 to form the y-axis. Lines from each of these marks can then be drawn to complete the grid.

Developing Numeracy
Using & Applying Maths
Year 6
© A & C BLACK

What's your angle?

Test your ideas and generalise

- ## You need a protractor and a ruler.

☆ The four circles below are all different sizes.
The **diameter** of each circle is marked.

☆ On each circle, draw a cross anywhere on its edge.
Use a ruler to join each end of the diameter
with the centre of your cross.

☆ Measure the angle where the lines meet at the cross.

- ## What do you notice? _____

- ## Do you think this is always true? _____

- ## Draw some circles of your own to check.
Use a pair of compasses.

Remember to draw the diameters.

Teachers' note Begin the lesson by revising how to measure angles in different orientations.
Demonstrate how a line can be extended if it is not long enough for the protractor. For the extension
activity, the children will need pairs of compasses.

Developing Numeracy
Using & Applying Maths
Year 6
© A & C BLACK

Shape shuffle: 1

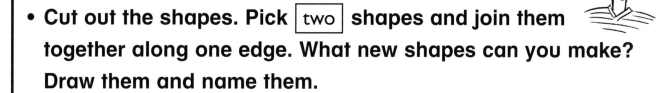

Your teacher will give you a set of shapes from *Shape shuffle: 2.*

- **Cut out the shapes. Pick** two **shapes and join them together along one edge. What new shapes can you make? Draw them and name them.**

trapezium   parallelogram

- **Now join** three **shapes together. What shapes can you make?**

You need a sheet of isometric paper.

- **Which three shapes can make a parallelogram <u>and</u> a trapezium?** _____ _____ _____

Teachers' note Revise the names and properties of quadrilaterals and other polygons. Give each child a set of shapes from page 40 and ask them to cut out the triangles, rhombi and trapeziums. When creating new shapes, make sure the children appreciate that the shapes must be joined along one complete side. They will need isometric paper or extra copies of the activity sheet for recording their shapes. See page 12 for solutions.

Developing Numeracy
Using & Applying Maths
Year 6
© A & C BLACK

Shape shuffle: 2

Record information, visualise and compare

Cut out the five sections. Each section provides three triangles, three rhombi and two trapeziums.

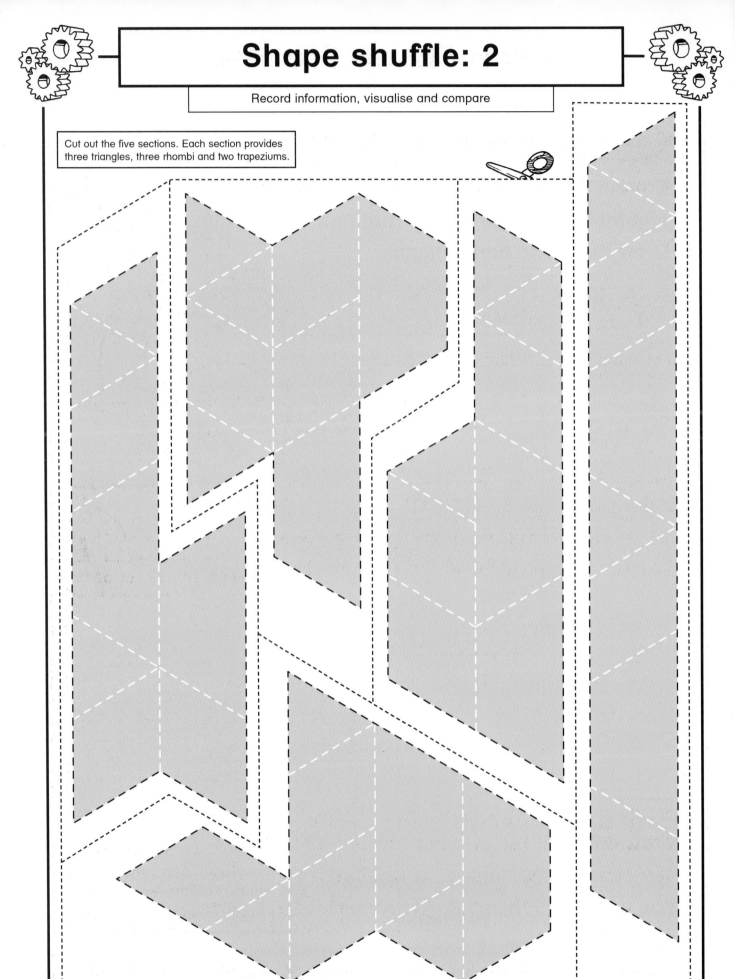

Teachers' note This sheet should be copied onto thin card and used with the activity on page 39. One sheet is sufficient for five children.

**Developing Numeracy
Using & Applying Maths
Year 6
© A & C BLACK**

Grow-Faster Granules

Simplify, reason and explain

- **Work with a partner to solve this problem.**

A carton of lawn food holds 1 kg of fertiliser granules.

It must be mixed with water.

Mix 100 g of fertiliser with 2 litres of water.

The mixture is sprinkled on the grass.

Oi!

The mixture made from 500 ml of water should cover 1 m² of grass.

Grow Faster

- **If the whole carton of fertiliser is mixed up, how many square metres of lawn will it cover?**

Show your workings here.

- **Draw different rectangular lawns that would use exactly this amount of fertiliser. You could use the scale 1 cm : 1 m.**

You need squared paper.

Now try this!

- **Write an explanation of how you solved this problem.**

Teachers' note Each pair needs one copy of the sheet, and squared paper. Allow them time to discuss the problem, and encourage them to simplify it by thinking of it in small steps: for example, first deciding how many lots of 100 g of fertiliser are in the carton. Once the extension activity has been completed, ensure the children have opportunities to listen to each other's explanations and to discuss differences in the approaches used.

**Developing Numeracy
Using & Applying Maths
Year 6
© A & C BLACK**

Vertex variations

Visualise

When you use a drawing program on a computer, you can drag a vertex of a shape to any dot on the screen.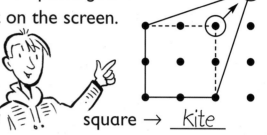

Look how this square changes into a kite when the circled vertex moves to another dot.

square → _Kite_

• **Imagine moving the circled vertex to other dots. Draw the shapes that the square changes into. Name the new shapes.**

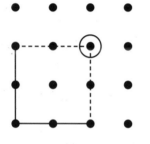

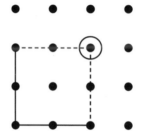

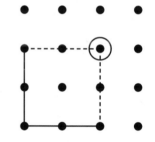

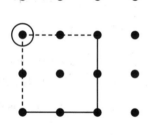

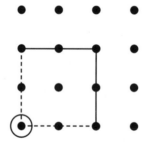

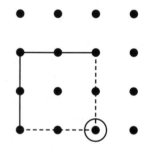

Now try this!

• **Change this trapezium into new shapes in the same way. Name the new shapes.**

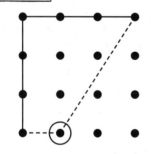

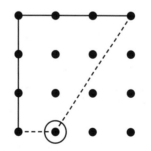

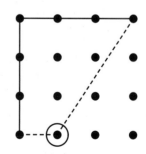

Teachers' note Revise the names and properties of quadrilaterals such as trapezium, kite, parallelogram and rhombus. It might be useful to display a list of the properties of each of the shapes. Remind the children that if a four-sided shape does not have any of these specific properties, then it is called a quadrilateral. As a further extension, the children could draw their own starting shapes on squared paper (such as right-angled triangle, parallelogram or pentagon) and repeat the activity.

**Developing Numeracy
Using & Applying Maths
Year 6
© A & C BLACK**

Time travel

Use trial and improvement

☆ Start on any space pad in the top row.

☆ Move from pad to pad, adding the times as you go.

☆ Try to find the route to the space station which has the smallest total time.

| 30 minutes | 15 minutes | 45 minutes | 15 minutes |

| 45 minutes | 30 minutes | 15 minutes | 45 minutes |

| 15 minutes | 45 minutes | 30 minutes | 15 minutes |

| 15 minutes | 30 minutes | 45 minutes | 10 minutes |

| 2 hours | 3 hours | 1 hour | 2 hours |

| 5 minutes | 50 minutes | 50 minutes | 20 minutes |

| 20 minutes | 40 minutes | 40 minutes | 25 minutes |

| 25 minutes | 20 minutes | 50 minutes | 40 minutes |

| 9 minutes | 5 minutes | 12 minutes | 18 minutes |

Now try this!

• **Find a route that totals exactly** 5 hours .

Teachers' note Encourage the children to try out different routes; they may find it helpful to use coloured pencils to mark off routes they have tried. Encourage them to look for ways to avoid large times, or to develop strategies that ensure the total time is low. The children could also explore other routes to find those that take up to 10 hours.

**Developing Numeracy
Using & Applying Maths
Year 6
© A & C BLACK**

43

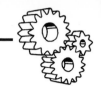

Crazy co-ordinates

- Use the digits in the box to make ⎨six⎬ different sets of co-ordinates. Use all the digits each time.
- On the grid, plot the two points in each set and join them with a straight line.

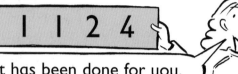

One set has been done for you.

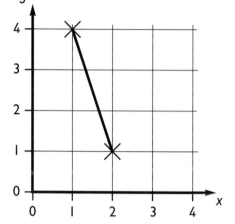

(2 , 1) and (1 , 4)   (,   ) and (,   )

(,   ) and (,   )   (,   ) and (,   )

(,   ) and (,   )   (,   ) and (,   )

- Talk to a partner about the pattern you have drawn.

- Find ⎨12⎬ different sets of co-ordinates. Plot the lines.

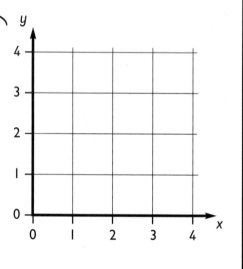

(,   ) and (,   )   (,   ) and (,   )

(,   ) and (,   )   (,   ) and (,   )

(,   ) and (,   )   (,   ) and (,   )

(,   ) and (,   )   (,   ) and (,   )

(,   ) and (,   )   (,   ) and (,   )

(,   ) and (,   )   (,   ) and (,   )

- Talk to a partner about the pattern you have drawn.

- Investigate the patterns for other sets of digits, like ⎨0 1 1 4⎬ or ⎨1 2 3 4⎬.

You need squared paper.

Teachers' note If necessary, remind the children how to write and plot co-ordinates. Ensure they understand that each set of co-ordinates must be different, and that (2, 1) and (4, 2) are the same as (4, 2) and (2, 1). Encourage a systematic approach. Provide mirrors so that the children can explore where the line of symmetry of the pattern is (along the diagonal line $x = y$).

Developing Numeracy
Using & Applying Maths
Year 6
© A & C BLACK

Talking angles

Explain and co-operate with others

On each card there is an angle.
• Try this activity with a partner.

☆ Cut out the cards. Spread them out face down.

☆ Pick a card. Describe the diagram for your partner
to draw on a piece of paper.

☆ Compare the drawing with your card. Is it accurate?

☆ Take turns to describe and draw.

Use words like these.

| right angle | acute | obtuse | estimate | degrees | vertex |
| horizontal line | vertical line | arc | N, S, E, W, NE, NW, SE, SW |

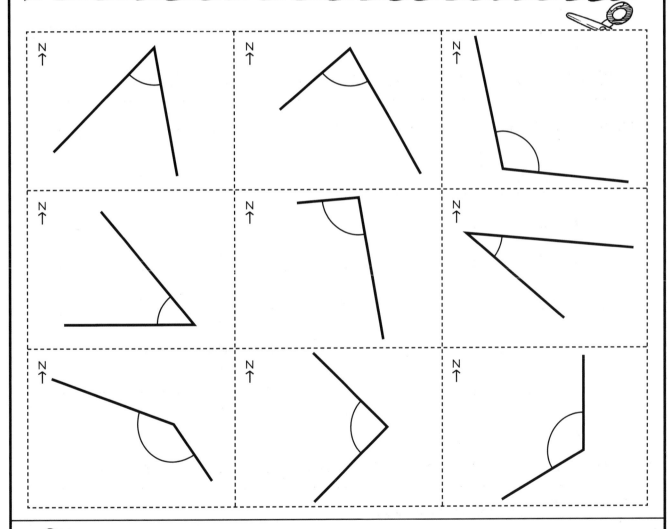

• Write a description of each card so that someone
else could pick it from the set.

Teachers' note Provide one sheet per pair, ideally copied onto card so that the diagrams cannot be seen through the paper. First ensure that the children understand the vocabulary in the box, including the compass points. Encourage the children to consider the orientation of the angle and to ensure that their partner's angle is drawn in the same way. They should estimate the size of angle and describe it using as much detail as possible, including estimates of approximate lengths of lines.

**Developing Numeracy
Using & Applying Maths
Year 6
© A & C BLACK**

Mass hysteria

Make estimates and co-operate with others

• Play this estimating game in a group.

☆ Your teacher will show you an object.

☆ In your group, estimate the mass of the object.

☆ Then write how many grams either side of this measurement you think it might be. The lower this number, the more points you could score.

☆ Your teacher will measure the actual mass. Write this down.

☆ Score 1 point if the actual mass is within the range you wrote down. Score 3 more points if your group's range was the smallest in the class.

pair of scissors	stapler	hole punch
Estimate: _____ g	**Estimate**: _____ g	**Estimate**: _____ g
or within _____ g either side of this.	or within _____ g either side of this.	or within _____ g either side of this.
Actual: _____ g	**Actual**: _____ g	**Actual**: _____ g
book	mug	bag of cubes
Estimate: _____ g	**Estimate**: _____ g	**Estimate**: _____ g
or within _____ g either side of this.	or within _____ g either side of this.	or within _____ g either side of this.
Actual: _____ g	**Actual**: _____ g	**Actual**: _____ g
calculator	roll of tape	5 rulers
Estimate: _____ g	**Estimate**: _____ g	**Estimate**: _____ g
or within _____ g either side of this.	or within _____ g either side of this.	or within _____ g either side of this.
Actual: _____ g	**Actual**: _____ g	**Actual**: _____ g

Now try this!

• **Estimate how many protractors will have a total mass of** $\boxed{1\ kg}$ **. Explain how you could work this out.**

Teachers' note Ask the children to work in groups of three or four. Give an example of how a group could make an estimate of say 250 g, but might allow themselves a range of 50 g either side. In this case they would score a point if the actual mass was between 200 g and 300 g inclusive, and they would score 3 bonus points if all the other groups chose ranges equal to or greater than 50 g. Weigh each object directly after the estimate is made, and before the mass of the next object is estimated.

**Developing Numeracy
Using & Applying Maths
Year 6
© A & C BLACK**

Peas, please

Reason, co-operate and make predictions

- ## Work with a partner or in a small group.

  You need thin card, sticky tape and some dried peas.

- ## Follow these instructions.

  ☆ On card, draw two identical rectangles, each with an area of 36 cm². Then cut them out. Do **not** draw squares.

  ☆ Write the lengths of the sides:

  length = _____ cm   width = _____ cm

  ☆ Roll the rectangles to make two different tubes. Tape the sides of each tube together **without** an overlap. Then tape over the bottom of each tube to make a container.

  ☆ Label the shorter, wider container **A**. Label the taller, thinner container **B**.

  ☆ Remember that the rectangles were identical. Do you think this means the containers will hold the same number of dried peas? Explain your answer.

  _____

  _____

  ☆ Estimate how many peas each container will hold.

  Container **A** will hold _____ peas.   Container **B** will hold _____ peas.

  ☆ Test your prediction. Write how many peas each container holds.

  Container **A** holds _____ peas.   Container **B** holds _____ peas.

- ## Repeat for other rectangles with areas of 36 cm², and this time include a square. Discuss what you notice.

Do all the containers hold the same number of peas?

If not, which types of containers hold the most?

What is special about containers made from a square?

Now try this!

- ## Write a report of what you found out.

Teachers' note If necessary, revise how to draw a rectangle with a given area. The children should agree on predictions before testing them to see whether they were correct. Dried beans or even cubes could be used instead of peas. During the plenary, encourage the children to suggest reasons why tins of food are the dimensions that they are.

**Developing Numeracy
Using & Applying Maths
Year 6
© A & C BLACK**

Troublesome triangles

☆ Work out how many different triangles there are in each pattern. Think about triangles of different shapes and sizes.

☆ Think of a way to show that you have found all the triangles in each pattern.

☆ Compare your solutions with a partner's.

> You could use coloured pencils to mark the triangles.

1.
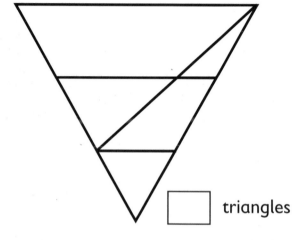
[ ] triangles

2.
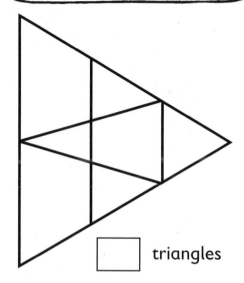
[ ] triangles

3.
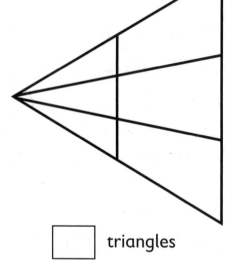
[ ] triangles

4.
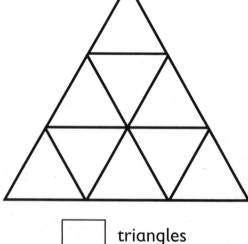
[ ] triangles

• **Draw your own triangle puzzle for a partner to solve (or choose a different shape such as a rectangle).**

> Make sure you know how many shapes there are.

Teachers' note Children often begin counting in a random way, and then lose count or forget whether they have counted a particular triangle already. It is important to encourage them to develop a more systematic approach: for example, choosing one line on the diagram and finding all the triangles that have this as its side, before moving on to a new line; looking at all the equilateral triangles first; or looking at all the triangles of a particular size first.

Developing Numeracy Using & Applying Maths Year 6 © A & C BLACK